Medical Vocation and Generation X

GW00683523

Jamie Harrison

GP Post-Graduate Tutor, Durham

Robert Innes

Lecturer in Systematic Theology at St John's College, Durham

GROVE BOOKS LIMITED
RIDLEY HALL RD CAMBRIDGE CB3 9HU

Contents

Foreword

This booklet has been jointly written throughout. Both authors are practitioners and academics. Jamie Harrison works as a GP and also trains doctors; Robert Innes is ordained and works in parish ministry as well as training clergy. In writing this booklet together it has been our hope that reflection on medical vocation might be enriched through dialogue with a sister profession.

The Cover Illustration is by Peter Ashton

First Impression July 1997
ISSN 0951-2659
ISBN 1 85174 348 0

1
Introduction

'I still regret it. It's a frightful price to pay for being good at science.'[1]

It might seem strange to begin a booklet on the nature of medical vocation with so pointedly negative a quotation. The psychiatric registrar's comment acts to summarize many of the careers of her contemporaries. Her biting view might seem out of place in a profession whose very essence would appear to be that of confident scientific virtue. Yet her vivid statement, full of poignant regretfulness, resonates with the experience of many who have set out on the journey towards acceptance into the medical profession.

One pertinent issue suggested by this conundrum is that of where medical vocation begins and in what way it is to be characterized. Does authentic vocation start with the archetypal, starry-eyed 18 year old interview candidate? She may feel a calling to change the universe for the better, care for those in need and find self-fulfilment on the way. But how are we to evaluate her youthful enthusiasm in the light of the newly registered house officer, all too often appearing cynical, brutalized and care-worn by early exposure to the medical world proper? And how is this to be compared with the established GP or consultant who may have regained much of the equilibrium of professionalism, of doing the job effectively, but may have sacrificed the last drop of idealism in the process?

The purpose of this study is to try to understand the pressures on a 'medical vocation for today' and to refashion such a concept for the doctors of tomorrow. The subject of our work originates in General Practice. However, GPs work within a culture defined more generally by the practices of the whole medical profession. What we write has a bearing on the profession as a whole.

We hope our work will be of interest principally to the following groups:

- Young people who are considering a career in medicine
- Individual doctors who may be struggling to articulate their own professional self-understanding
- Leaders within the medical profession who seek to shape its future direction.

The issues raised also resonate with other caring professionals, notably clergy, where the vocational questions are similar. Indeed, the question of medical vocation is part of a more widely felt 'crisis of work' in contemporary society.[2] We will note comparisons with other professions where they seem especially apposite.

This booklet is written from a Christian perspective, and one of the authors is a theologian. Contemporary medicine has emerged as a largely secular discipline

---

1 I Allen, *Doctors and their Careers: A New Generation* (London: Policy Studies Institute, 1994) p 233.
2 See, for example, the discussion of contemporary working life in the report published by the Council of Churches for Britain and Ireland, *Unemployment and the Future of Work* (Apr 1997).

espousing rational principles and resting on a body of empirical, scientific data and theory. But one does not need to look far to discover quite deep relationships between medicine and religion. In the medieval period, the Christian church sponsored the work of healing through its monasteries. Modern medical science itself arose in the context of a Christian religious world-view, an outlook on life many doctors still hold today. It is our genuine hope that what we write will be of interest to those who do not share this world-view. And those who hold different beliefs may profit through their own constructive critique of our position.

The present booklet is one of a series entitled 'Ethical Studies.' This may be misleading. We are not trying to formulate ethical principles or codes, but rather to explore the context within which ethical medical thinking takes place. The notion of vocation (*vocatio*) is an auricular one, suggesting a life lived as response to an invitation or call. What one perceives to be the content of the invitation will determine, at a high level, how one responds practically and ethically.

We shall also employ visual images or 'characters.' William May describes well how proper moral reflection entails a knowledgeable re-visioning of foundations and ends.[3] It is the activity of learning to see ourselves correctly and clearly. Rethinking the content of the *vocatio* can equally be considered as the recapturing of a *vision* of the doctor. An image provides a normative definition of the social role of the doctor. It also generates a metaphysical setting in which people act out or improvise from a basic script or character.

Alasdair MacIntyre distinguishes a 'character' from a mere social role in that the former, but not the latter, places a certain kind of moral constraint on the personality of those who inhabit it.[4] Many occupational roles, those of dentist or refuse collector for instance, are not (on MacIntyre's use of the term) characters since they do not embody a particular set of moral attitudes. By contrast, in the case of a character, the social role and personality of the individual fuse so as to limit possible ranges of action. MacIntyre argues that what is specific to a culture is, in large part, what is embodied in its stock of characters. So, he suggests, the culture of Victorian England was partially defined by the characters of the Public School Headmaster, the Explorer and the Engineer. A character furnishes his or her contemporaries with a cultural and moral ideal; they use the character to understand and to evaluate themselves.

Rethinking medical vocation involves clarifying the 'character' of the doctor. In view of their high public esteem doctors are still, in some sense, regarded as figures of moral authority. But it is less clear precisely what set of attributes and characteristics the doctor is supposed to possess. Indeed, as we shall shortly see, much of the difficulty with sustaining a 'vocation' to medicine lies in the sharp conflict between the traditional attributes of the doctor and those which seem to be in vogue in the contemporary, allegedly postmodern, world.

3   William F May, *The Physician's Covenant: Images of the Healer in Medical Ethics* (Philadelphia: Westminster Press, 1983) p 14ff.
4   Alasdair MacIntyre, *After Virtue* (London: Duckworth, 1981) p 27ff.

2
A Postmodern Context:
Generation X or Generation Why?

The arrival of postmodernity was famously described by Jean-François Lyotard as a suspicion of 'grand narratives,' that is, the failure of generally agreed overarching systems of morality or rationality by which we can understand ourselves and the world. The implications of postmodernity for a notion of medical vocation are serious, and some of them are as follows.

- *The de-legitimization of science.* Hitherto we have seen science, including medical science, as a universally applicable, ideologically neutral, body of knowledge. Postmodernity encourages us to be suspicious of this kind of claim. Science is seen by the postmodernists as a means of exerting power and control. Casting doubt on the objective truth of medical science encourages the development of alternative therapies and medicines—everything from acupuncture, herbal remedies and homeopathy, to the amazing curative powers of magnetic bracelets. The trend to postmodernity subverts the distinctive credentials and status of the orthodox doctor.
- *Fragmentation of the self.* The psychologist Stephen Frosh comments, 'Perhaps the most generally accepted characteristic of the modern mind is that it is a condition in which the "struggle to be a self" is nearly impossible.'[5] Without some coherent 'narrative' to explain ourselves to ourselves, life becomes a series of discrete moments, a collage built up of fragments, which may have little relation to one another. There is an emphasis on the transient, the ephemeral, the fleeting. Once we start to understand ourselves in such a way, it becomes difficult to sustain commitment to a lifetime's vocation.
- *The priority of pleasure and desire.* Several of the fashionable postmodernist authors describe human beings in terms of the need to satisfy basic desires. The cult book *Anti-Oedipus* opens with a graphic and disturbing account of the human being as a machine built up out of smaller 'desiring machines.'[6] For the authors, human persons are to be described merely as a series of states of desire. Again, the influential postmodernist Michel Foucault offers a *History of Sexuality* in which the aim is to discover an ethic which assigns a major role to the creative use of pleasure.[7] This kind of writing encourages a culture in which consumption, and the meeting of desire, is attended to far more carefully than

5   Stephen Frosh, *Identity Crisis: Modernity, Psychoanalysis and the Self* (London: Routledge, 1991) p 5.
6   Gilles Deleuze and Félix Guattari, *Anti-Oedipus: Capitalism and Schizophrenia* (Minneapolis: University of Minnesota, 1992).
7   Michel Foucault, *History of Sexuality Vols 1, 2 and 3* (London: Penguin, 1990 and 1992).

the mechanics of production. In such a culture, committing oneself to a vocation may be understood as simply missing out on life.

Generation X...

One of the 'characters' by which we can understand postmodernity is the inhabitant of 'Generation X.' The term 'Generation X' was first used to describe the 1960s hippies, but it has achieved a new social definition in Douglas Copeland's *Generation X: Tales for an Accelerated Culture*.

'Andy, Dag and Claire have been handed a society priced beyond their means. Twentysomethings, brought up with divorce, Watergate and Three Mile Island, and scarred by the 80s fall-out of yuppies, recession, crack and Ronald Reagan, they represent the new generation—Generation X. Fiercely suspicious of being lumped together as an advertiser's target market, they have quit dreary careers and cut themselves adrift in the Californian desert. Unsure of their futures, they immerse themselves in a regime of heavy drinking and working at no-future McJobs in the service industry.'[8]

Generation X are the generation born since 1960. They follow the post-World War II 'baby-boomers.' Generation Xers have grown up in a world of computers, video, the latch key and the acceptance of leisure as a way of life. Jobs are no longer for life, contracts are short-term and the idea of a mortgage or serious commitment needs careful thought.

...or Generation Why?

Claims that the postmodern era has truly arrived—with complete loss of confidence in science, disappearance of an integrated sense of self and abject moral relativism—are much overstated. What we can affirm is that we live in an era of greater fragmentation. The pace of change is faster, and short-term gratification wins against long-term goals. This prevailing sense of fluidity generates a deep questioning of many norms that a previous generation took for granted. We live in an age of uncertainty. The rising generation could be termed 'Generation Why?'

In the medical world, the new generation manifests itself by travelling round the world after the first hospital jobs, looking to work less than full time and being wary of settling into a fixed pattern 'just yet.' The general flavour is of a greater willingness to 'get a life'—which may mean questioning wholesale dedication to that all-demanding medical career.

There is a new demand for flexibility. Already, over half the newly qualified doctors in the UK are women. They have particular needs to take career breaks and to have flexible work patterns. The men also see the benefits of flexibility and fluidity. Economic success may no longer be the goal of many who value the

---

8   Douglas Copeland, *Generation X: Tales for an Accelerated Culture* (London: Abacus, 1992), cover blurb.

freedom to pursue interests and concerns beyond the purely medical. There is a desire to find fulfilment not just through one's job, but in many sectors of life—for example, one's family, cultural pursuits, friendships and an inner spiritual life.

The post-baby-boomers have been accused of being the slackers' generation, unwilling to work hard and looking for the low paid, menial 'McJob' rather than taking proper responsibility and putting in the hours. This view has been refuted with some vigour.[9] Generation Xers may well be prepared to put in the necessary effort but they need a say in the purpose of the work. They demand proper training, career options and flexibility. They will not follow blindly or just do things because 'that is how we have always done it.'

The new ethos represented by the rising generation of medical recruits poses some hard questions for 'medical vocation.' In an article entitled, 'Doctors and Commitment: Nice work—shame about the job' two of those responsible for training GPs put the matter like this:

'Commitment must express the sort of people we want to be as well as what things seem worthwhile to do. Although as doctors we are taught to take a good history from our patients, our own histories often remain hidden from us. Hitherto we have not needed to be clear about our personal and professional needs and aims, but now we must recognize and explain what lies deeper than current economic and political fashion, and [must] make our goals explicit.'[10]

In the following section we therefore try to articulate some of the 'history' that lies embedded in a traditional understanding of medical vocation, so that we can better understand how far it might be sustained amidst contemporary pressures and how it might need to be modified.

9   B Tulgan, *Managing Generation X: How to Bring out the Best in Young Talent* (Oxford: Capstone, 1996).
10 Clare Vaughan and Roger Higgs, *BMJ* Vol 311 23-30, December 1995, p 1655.

3
The Traditional Image of the Doctor as Self-Sacrificing Parent

The medical profession embodies a strong ethic of benevolent service to humanity. This comes to formal expression in a number of recent international codes of ethics. For example:

'A PHYSICIAN SHALL, in all types of medical practice, be dedicated to providing competent medical service in full technical and moral independence, with compassion and respect for human dignity...'

'A PHYSICIAN SHALL owe his patients complete loyalty and all the resources of his science...'

'A PHYSICIAN SHALL give emergency care as a humanitarian duty unless he is assured that others are willing and able to give such care.'[11]

Or again:

'It is the privilege of the medical doctor to practise medicine in the service of humanity...'[12]

And an older code states that members of the medical profession are those 'upon whom is enjoined the performance of so many arduous duties toward the community, and who are required to make so many sacrifices of comfort, ease, and health, for the welfare of those who avail themselves of their services.'[13]

These codes express an ideal of unstinting and selfless service to the needy. In some codes, this ideal is expressed in terms which have distinctly religious, even missionary, overtones. For example: 'It is the mission of the medical doctor to safeguard the health of the people. His or her knowledge and conscience are dedicated to the fulfilment of this mission.'[14] The obligation to safeguard the health of the people is a boundless duty.

The sacred duty of the doctor finds particularly strong expression in the Declaration of Geneva, which opens: 'At the time of being admitted to the medical

---

11 'International Code of Medical Ethics' (World Medical Association, 1949, 1968, 1983) in Melanie Phillips and John Dawson, *Doctors' Dilemmas: Medical Ethics and Contemporary Science* (Brighton: Harvester, 1985) p 206f.
12 The Declaration of Tokyo (World Medical Association, 1975) *ibid*, p 218.
13 American Medical Association (1847) quoted in May *The Physician's Covenant* p 93.
14 The Declaration of Helsinki (World Medical Association, 1964, 1975) *ibid*, p 212.

profession: 'I solemnly pledge my life to the service of humanity,' and which continues: 'The health of my patient will be my first consideration.'[15]

Now, to some extent, these kinds of codes are the product of official bodies with whom most doctors have very little, if any, contact. Such lofty pronouncements may have little direct influence on the way a doctor typically goes about his or her work. Indeed, a straw poll of doctors, when asked, could not remember what, if anything, they had promised at the time of being admitted to their profession! Nonetheless such codes do form a basic expression of professional identity; the lengthy consultative processes by which they were formulated and agreed reflect the presence of a general sense of extraordinarily selfless, humanitarian vocation.[16]

If most of us have little direct acquaintance with worldwide medical codes of ethics we nonetheless have a picture in our cultural memory of a doctor who embodies the spirit of such an ethic.

The ideal of the family doctor was of a man (occasionally it might have been a woman) who had personal knowledge of every member of one's family and their history. He saw his patients from the front room of his large, comfortable house. Along with the vicar, he was one of the few highly educated figures in the village. He was an authority figure, someone one's family might turn to in time of need—especially, of course, in the event of physical illness—but perhaps on other matters as well. The doctor was someone to whom you unhesitatingly gave your respect. Think of Dr Cameron in the television series *Dr Finlay's Casebook*.

In return for his special status in the community the doctor gave patients his benevolent and unceasing care. He would come out immediately if they had need of him, whatever the time of day or night. His personal identity merged into his professional role. The title 'Doctor' did not refer to his academic qualifications but was the way one addressed the particular character—much the same as the mode of addressing the 'Vicar.' Whatever his domestic circumstances or private interests they were fashioned within the embracing and over-riding 'character' of the doctor.

This doctor is in effect a self-sacrificing 'parent' for the community. He offers the humane, personal care of the good father or mother. Without need of explanation he addresses patients by their first name. He assumes a level of physical intimacy that no-one else, other than a close family member, presumes. He embodies the self-expenditure and compassion which are the marks of the good parent.

The paternal image finds expression in a similar way in the clergyman who, despite biblical injunctions to the contrary, likes to be called 'Father.' Just as the

---

15 World Medical Association, 1948, 1968, 1983, cited in Phillips and Dawson, p 211.
16 One might compare, as a point of contrast, the very modest opening statement of ethical principle governing the world's largest professional firm of accountants and management consultants: 'The paramount ethical standard of The Arthur Andersen Worldwide Organization is that each partner and employee must maintain his or her integrity and objectivity.' (Arthur Andersen & Co Ethical Standards 1983 Article 1.3).

people are dependent on the doctor for their bodily well-being, so they are dependent on the clergyman for their spiritual well-being. The clergyman's very title (Vicar) speaks of his self-sacrificial willingness to bear the cares and concerns of his flock.

Robin Greenwood describes how this paternal image of the clergyman proved hugely influential in fostering models of theological training up until the 1970s. Greenwood identifies a series of theological college principals (more especially from the Anglo-Catholic tradition) who modelled through their own lives a demanding pattern of vocation, focused on pastoral care. For example, Greenwood comments in respect of B K Cunningham, Principal of Westcott House (1919-34), that he inspired in his students (whom he referred to as his 'boys') 'that sense of service to humanity, at whatever personal cost, which has been a prevailing characteristic of the upper middle class Christian-inspired ethic for much of the twentieth century.'[17]

Within the Christian tradition, this ideal of fatherly self-sacrifice is typically justified with reference to the imitation of Christ, the supreme self-giver. Self-sacrifice becomes the principle which overrides all others. The key arbiter becomes the answer to the question, 'What would Christ have done in this situation? How should I put the needs of others before myself?'

Critique

The character of the village family doctor who attended to his people as part of a vocation that embodied fatherly self-sacrifice is, to a significant extent, a nostalgic myth. People knew that you did not visit the doctor unless there was something seriously wrong. You might have to pay for treatment. And you could expect an irate response if he felt you were wasting his time. Access to the doctor was restricted, both by the aura of patriarchal and professional respect and by a fearsome receptionist (possibly his wife). Moreover, this doctor lived before the age of potentially constant access granted by the mobile phone.

There remains a need for the doctor to be a benevolent figure of authority. Particularly in economically deprived areas, the medical institutions act to give shape and meaning to the community. The local hospital and GP surgery function to provide order and a place of safety for those needing reassurance and access to health care. The interconnected network of primary and secondary providers of medical treatment acts to hold together a society unsure of where it is going and fearful of the next challenge it faces. Increasingly in the inner city, doctors and ministers, along with social workers and teachers, are the only professionals left to care and to belong.

However, the notion of doctor as self-sacrificing parent cannot be sustained in the contemporary world. The myth of constant availability could only be maintained when the doctor knew that patients would not act as if it were true. One GP recently quipped that 'doctors offered everything on the basis that patients

---

17 Robin Greenwood, *Transforming Priesthood* (London: SPCK, 1994) p 26.

would not ask too much.'[18]

The protective aura of patriarchal respect is now disappearing. The modern emphasis on personal autonomy and freedom leads us to treat those who claim to be benevolent authority figures with suspicion. We are rightly reluctant to enter into relations which presuppose and foster our dependence on someone else.[19] Claims to authority must now be rationally justified. We prefer to enter into relationships with professionals where it is clear what are the expectations and rights on both sides.

In addition, we live in a climate of continually rising expectations for standards of health and medical care. Health care has become something of a 'product,' delivered by an increasingly sophisticated technology to an ever more health-conscious population. The doctor who continues to operate as a beneficent parent figure, who relies on historical authority and neglects ongoing personal development and training, may be courting disaster. For today's patients are keenly aware of the possibilities of contemporary medicine, and increasingly intolerant of doctors who do not deliver the highest quality. A mistaken or belated diagnosis may shatter the esteem with which the patients endow the doctor. Instead of being regarded as a benevolent patrician the doctor comes to be seen as dangerously out of date.

The ethic of unstinting self-sacrifice still persists in the medical profession, but often with very unfortunate results. One way it is manifested is in the appallingly long hours which were, for a long time, tolerated amongst junior doctors. This is a symptom of a generally 'macho' approach to their own ability to keep going. Doctors are not allowed to be ill. They deny problems, self-medicate and stay on the job 'for the patients' benefit.' This behaviour, which is inappropriate for all sorts of reasons, needs to be challenged. The lack of a proper occupational health service for doctors is indicative of the problem and compounds it. Inadequate arrangements to provide cover for sick doctors, as well as those on holiday or study leave, is another related issue. A falsely heroic view of self-sacrifice can present real dangers to patients and doctors alike.

From a theological perspective, the self-sacrificing ethic has come under severe criticism in recent years. It can far too easily be employed in oppressive and destructive ways. Critics point to the manner in which the quasi-religious ideal of self-sacrifice was employed by Adolf Hitler in his exhortations to the people of Germany to defend the fatherland. If you are going to sacrifice yourself you must be absolutely sure that the end is the right one. Again, feminists have pointed out how the ideal of self-sacrifice can serve an ideology in which a whole section of society, such as women, are kept in a subordinate position.

In the professional sphere, a purported commitment to a self-sacrificial vocation is frequently used as a means by which senior staff exert unfair moral pressure on

---

18 Vaughan and Higgs, *BMJ* 311, p 1654.
19 In this respect, the influence of the educational model set out in Rousseau's *Emile* cannot be overestimated.

juniors. Thus the consultant berates the junior hospital doctor who protests against having to work for excessive periods without rest on the grounds that he lacks the requisite level of commitment. In the clerical profession, there are many instances of bishops interpreting the notion of vocation as a licence to redeploy junior staff wherever and whenever they choose. To switch the grounds of argument from, 'Is this request reasonable or not?' to, 'Are you or are you not prepared to be faithful to your [self-sacrificing] vocation?' is a move which a newer generation of professionals is not so willing to accept. It is, of course, one thing to dedicate oneself to a professional cause and quite another to have a superior tell you that the terms of this dedication involve certain demanding courses of action which seem convenient and reasonable to the superior but not to you.

In the light of these severe difficulties, it is not surprising that the whole concept of medical vocation easily appears anachronistic. It belongs to an era when certain privileged individuals could lay claim to a professional calling which granted them automatic status and respect. In today's climate it appears to be a means of laying oneself open to exploitation. And it does not seem to account for the specialization consequent upon technological change.

One major response to these problems is to abandon or sideline the notion of vocation in favour of other models or images. In the following section we explore some of the most significant of these other ways of conceiving the medical profession.

4
Alternative Images of the Doctor

The Technician

According to one definition, a profession is 'a vocation, a calling, especially one requiring advanced knowledge or training in some branch of learning or science.'[20] Here the notion of vocation is qualified with respect to the possession of a definite body of advanced knowledge. Within the medical world itself, there are some for whom it is the possession of technical knowledge, rather than the sense of calling or vocation, that is the defining characteristic of the profession.

The technical nature of the profession is strongly emphasized in the way that doctors are trained. Until recently, at the start of his or her training the medical student was introduced not to a group of live patients whom the student would learn how to heal, but to a cadaver which the student would learn to dissect. Premedical training continued with an almost exclusive focus on the acquisition of specialist scientific facts and knowledge. Still, today, medicine remains one of the few subjects in the university which is examined by means of multiple choice questions. Implicitly, and sometimes explicitly, the student learns that the highest tier of the profession is for those who go into scientific research and teaching. The next tier is for those who aspire to specialist consultant posts in the hospitals. Finally, there is a remainder who go into General Practice. The greatest professional status tends to accrue to those who have the highest degree of technical specialism. This ranking has the unfortunate effect of according relatively low status to those who have the most contact with the whole patient.[21]

The 'character' of the technician is, indeed, a very persuasive and appealing one. Modern medicine is perhaps the greatest of the scientific success stories of the century and it generates respect for those who are associated with it. Of course, not all technicians have high status. The electronic engineer working in military defence and the research chemist developing new plastics are certainly experts in their fields, but they do not have the same kind of public recognition as the doctor. It somehow seems more difficult to speak of one's vocation to be a metallurgist than one's vocation to be a doctor. By contrast with other technicians, the doctor employs his or her skills in a profession which seems self-evidently to be directed in the service of a good cause—the relief of sickness and suffering. He or she still carries the aura of public benevolence. The doctor is not a technician like other scientists; for he unites (or so it seems) power and knowledge with philanthropy.

---

20 *The New Shorter Oxford English Dictionary.*
21 And does not seem to do justice to the fact that 90% of medical contacts are in General Practice!

13

Critique

Technical competency, possession of accurate and up-to-date knowledge of one's field, is a key requirement for being a good doctor. Despite tendencies towards a 'supermarket' of orthodox, quasi-orthodox and alternative therapies, most patients still have a clear idea of what constitutes a 'real' doctor. The essence of quackery remains pretending to technical qualifications that one does not possess. Thus the *Sunday Express* newspaper has for some time been running a campaign to expose bogus medical specialists operating from Harley Street.[22] What makes the stories of scandalous interest is the mismatch between the popular notion of Harley Street as a centre of medical excellence, and the possibility of individuals not performing according to, or in some cases falsifying, their technical qualifications. The fear some have experienced about being treated by a doctor when one is in a foreign country is primarily due to uncertainty about whether or nor the doctor possesses the kind of qualifications that would make him or her a 'real' doctor in the UK.

Nonetheless, a devotion to the *technique* of medicine can never be fully adequate, for the following reasons.

Firstly, an undue focus on technique can be a way of *escaping from the demands of persons*. For example, a doctor may dwell heavily on the details of a specific treatment regime for a cancer patient as a way of avoiding the wider, and more distressing, questions of the overall health of the patient and his or her family. For clergy, a similar tactic may be employed in taking a difficult funeral: one deliberately distances oneself from the emotions of the persons involved by concentrating on the performance of the rite. In such situations some degree of distancing may well be necessary, but if the recipient senses a deliberate withdrawal the impression is quickly conveyed of coldness and lack of care.

Secondly, exaltation of technique may simply be a way of *dodging the more difficult vocational questions*. Devotion to the art and refinement of one's skills can be a way of evading the higher level questions about whether what one is doing is worthwhile. This is readily observed in the software engineer who takes delight in the elegance of her solutions but is uninterested in the question of whether the upgrade to the invoice processing module of the batch accounting system is of any real value. Likewise some clergy can devote themselves to a professional performance of the liturgy without wanting to face the painful question of whether anyone is listening to what they are saying.

Thirdly, some of the most typical illnesses which confront the GP *do not yield themselves to technical solutions*. Many illnesses have social causes. A large proportion of patients suffer from complaints rooted in, for example, smoking, obesity, alcohol abuse, minor drug abuse or inadequate housing. These kinds of problems may require long term primary healthcare and education of whole communities

---

2 2 For example the double page article (p 36f) on Sunday April 13th 1997 billed as 'How I became a Harley Street doctor in 48 hours.' Harley Street is popularly perceived as the area from which London's leading medical specialists practise.

into healthy ways of life. Here the doctor may need to work in partnership with local community groups and other professionals such as nurses and social workers. The emphasis on technology tends to encourage doctors towards the glamorous world of CT scanners and intensive-therapy units to the detriment of fundamental programmes of health care in the community.

The Manager

Within the NHS, doctors have always been responsible for the stewardship of resources. A doctor who is paid out of public funds is responsible to society at large for the way he or she allocates professional time between patients. The family doctor may have been part of a small partnership, with a receptionist to be paid, a surgery to maintain and accounts to be prepared. Each free prescription that was written implicitly required some judgment as to whether or not this was a wise use of public money. One of the roles of the GP has always been that of 'gatekeeper,' judging which patients should be referred on to the relatively expensive care offered by the hospital specialists.

However, increasing demand for health care has sharply raised awareness of finite public resources. The government's main strategy for managing a potentially limitless demand has been to introduce market economics into the NHS. Whereas in the past resources were rationed by the covert method of the waiting list, there has been a sharp move towards more explicit allocation based on the ability of a medical 'purchaser' to pay a medical 'provider.' As a result, doctors now find themselves much more consciously involved in the management of health care resources.

From the patient's point of view, evidence of a willingness amongst doctors to adopt a managerial identity is readily at hand. For example, a large medical practice in Durham recently relocated from its cosy and traditional (if cramped) surgery to new premises which appear from the outside to resemble the headquarters of a small computer software house. There is a large foyer, staffed by a team of receptionists, adjacent to a comfortable waiting area. Somewhere in the background one hears the murmur of telephonists. Each of the doctors occupies an office equipped with executive chair, desk and PC. On the second floor are seminar rooms with chairs set around central desks, in the model of a training room in a commercial enterprise. The operation is under the direction of a practice manager. On attending an appointment for some minor ailment or other, the doctor may offer some 'valued-added' services—a well-man check perhaps, or some injections for the foreign holiday.

This is an era in which doctors seem happy to talk about 'patient management,' 'trauma management' and 'grief management.' Potentially overwhelming patient demands are managed through contracts. Thus junior doctors have contracts limiting their hours of service. GP practices buy into agency services that provide night-time call-out cover over a wide geographical area.

Critique

The 'manager' is one of the stock characters of modern society and managerialism has become an enormously significant mode of practice in our culture. The manager trades in efficiency and effectiveness. In the medical world the manager's competence may be measured in such things as the length of hospital waiting lists, queuing times in the surgery, control of waste, patient 'throughput.'

We are well used to thinking of effectiveness and efficiency as non-moral qualities. Thus we suppose that to ask about the efficiency of the doctor is to ask a quite different kind of question from inquiring about the ends to which the doctor's craft is put—judging, for example, the moral evil of Auschwitz's Dr Mengele. It seems, at first sight, obvious that the doctor should be as efficient as possible, and that we can argue about the morality of the profession as a separate exercise.

However, as MacIntyre points out, there are strong grounds for rejecting the claim that effectiveness is a morally neutral value. 'Effectiveness is a defining and definitive element of a way of life which competes for our allegiance with other alternative contemporary ways of life.'[23] To give a large-scale example, a health authority may decide to merge two hospitals, thereby depriving a relatively poorly-off community of its local accident and emergency department. Such a decision is typically justified on the grounds that the new services can be delivered 'more efficiently.' But, as protest campaigns testify, this is never an adequate answer to moral questions of social justice and rights to proximate access to health care.

For the individual doctor a 'managerial attitude' may conflict significantly with what he or she takes to be a primary responsibility of care for patients. The manager works to maximize the profit of a corporation. His or her primary loyalty is to the employer. By contrast, the doctor works to heal patients and his or her primary loyalty ought to be to them. The imposition of managerial discipline is one way in which the employer (directly or indirectly the government) brings unruly professional groups into line. Unsurprisingly, many doctors have found the process extremely painful.[24]

There are many misconceptions involved in the ascription to doctors, by society and by themselves, of the character of the manager:
- Health is not a commodity like other commodities. Health cannot be freely purchased or sold in the marketplace independently of the persons to whom it pertains.
- It is inadequate to model the relationship between doctor and patient in terms of a contract freely entered into by a supplier and a buyer. Such a model fails to account for:

a) The flexibility required to accommodate a myriad of possible develop-

---

2 3 MacIntyre, *After Virtue* , p 74.

2 4 See, for example, the survey (*Committed but Critical*) of doctors under the age of 40 compiled and written by Isobel Allen (of the Policy Studies Institute) and published by the BMA in April 1997. Allen paints an alarming picture of doctors driven by 'managers with clipboards' to maintain throughput and to account for their time. She suggests that commitment to theri patients is the only thing which is keeping many younger doctors from leaving the profession.

ments of the patient's condition.

b) The huge imbalance of power between a doctor (who has potential control over the patient's health, happiness and longevity) and the patient (who inevitably confronts the doctor in a position of ignorance at a moment of personal weakness).[25]

- A commercial manager will only enter into business deals where he or she can make a profit and will walk away from those where a loss is expected. By contrast, we rightly expect doctors to enrol and treat patients irrespective of their 'profitability' to the practice.

- It makes a huge difference to the quality of the doctor-patient relationship if the patient suspects that the doctor's main interest is in meeting some managerial objective. I will regard the doctor's prescriptions and treatment quite differently if I think that he is partly motivated by his desire to make money out of me. Whatever we think of the introduction of contractual arrangements in non-medical services in the NHS, political moves to subject *medical* services to contractual discipline are rightly suspect. The prospect of doctors competing with each other to offer the most cost-effective treatment is deeply unattractive.

---

25 Notwithstanding the possibility that, after the medical encounter, a patient might seek legal redress if it turns out that the doctor's power had been negligently or improperly used. It is doubtful how much patients feel empowered when they are actually under the care of the doctor, by the knowledge that they could sue if the doctor gets it wrong. At the limit the patient is aware that, whereas she could, for example, sue a mechanic if he makes a mess of repairing her car, she might not be around to sue if the doctor makes a serious mistake with her health.

5

Towards a New Understanding of Vocation: The Doctor as Covenanter

The Sense of Being Chosen

We would all like to think that we are in control of our own destinies. Whatever our philosophical or religious views, we want to believe that decisions we have taken over the years have been based on reasonable and rational criteria. The 'technician' and 'manager' characters both exemplify this kind of rational thinking. We suppose that we can plan and manage our lives ahead of us according to specific criteria which we freely choose. Organizing one's future is thought to be a matter of completing the 'goals' and 'tasks' sections of one's Time Manager filofax.

But life is, in practice, more complex than this. In ordinary life we do not deal in certainties of a demonstrable order, but rather in commitments which we do not choose. We think we make choices but we seldom pause to think what causes us to want. There is a complex process whereby we are summoned out of indifference and indecision and caught up in some practice or other. Until you have been 'summoned,' there is no interest in a particular quarter. You may know that other people have a particular interest, but it contains no interest for you and you do not bother to find out anything about it.[26]

The experience of becoming a doctor suggests that much more is going on than merely my free choice of a career. Young people apply to medical school with all sorts of hopes and expectations. They may well not see the influence of subconscious thoughts and motivations. Occasionally they may believe that special factors have influenced them, whether through the advice of friends and family or even the intervention of forces beyond their control. Applicants invariably have excellent A level grades, a wide expertise with, for instance, musical instruments and a long list of social accomplishments. These are the brightest and the best and many are disappointed not to be offered places. Knowledge of what the job entails and a long-held desire to be a doctor herald a greater chance of ultimate qualification and a career in medicine. The tough selection procedure is already choosing the few and rejecting the many. Acceptance itself may generate a sense of 'rightness'; when the door opens to me I feel confirmed in the sense that my putting my hand to the latch was appropriate.

Acceptance marks the beginning of a process of formation. Students soon become caught up in the excitement of each speciality. One discipline rapidly follows another, one assessment system following the last. Career ideas come and go as every specialism vies for supremacy. All too quickly, the final examinations

---

2 6 As more fully argued by Timothy Jenkins in an unpublished paper 'Community and Vocation.'

are arriving and decisions about the first medical job loom. A vague notion of vocation has become subsumed in this thing called medicine. The reflective student may well sense that, whilst all along thinking she was in control, she actually feels called and shaped by some much larger forces. The experience of being 'laid hold on' is well expressed in the saying of Jesus, 'You did not choose me but I chose you' (John 15.16). It is this strange combination of one's own conscious leanings (inevitably only partially informed), with the sense of being seized by something greater which is so well captured by the notion of 'vocation.'

Theological Challenges to the Notion of Vocation

The use of the term vocation to describe commitment to a form of work (as distinct from an interior spiritual calling) derives from Martin Luther and has developed within Protestant theology as a principal means of understanding the relation of the worker to his or her work.[27] However, it has recently become subject to considerable criticism within its native tradition—perhaps the most important example of which is Miroslav Volf's book *Work in the Spirit*.[28] We list his major criticisms here, and suggest that, however pertinent they might be in respect of work in general, they are not convincing in the case of medicine. Volf's principal arguments are that:

1. *Vocation is a category which is indifferent to alienation in work.* Whilst this criticism must be taken seriously, say, in respect of production-line workers, the notion of alienation does not have significant bearing on the work of a doctor, who is treating patients rather than making objects for profit.
2. *Vocation can easily be misused ideologically to justify soulless kinds of work.* This criticism points to the need for work itself to be placed within a higher ethical framework, so that vocation cannot be used as a rationale for exploitation.
3. *Vocation is not applicable to an increasingly mobile society where people may change jobs several times during their lifetime.* Change of work to an unrelated field is likely to occur less often for doctors than for those in other kinds of work, in view of the very long and intensive training period to which the doctor commits. However, the notion of vocation must not be used to justify a static notion of work, but must be open to the possibility of one's work developing and changing.
4. *Vocation does not allow for a plurality of employment.* As Volf admits, Luther himself was not consistent on this point, and there seems no reason why the idea of vocation could not allow for multiple vocations (say as doctor, wife, mother, daughter and churchwarden).
5. *The notion of vocation has historically contributed to the divinization of work.* Volf is right that we suffer from a contemporary over-valuation of work which risks

---

27 See, for example, John Goldingay and Robert Innes, *God at Work I* (Grove Ethical Studies No 94, Nottingham: Grove Books, 1994).
28 Oxford: OUP, 1991. See especially pp 107ff.

becoming a religion of total work.[29] However, the Lutheran doctrine of vocation is only one of the contributors to this, and may not be the most significant.
Some of the strongest exhortations to a life of total work come from Romantic
authors such as Thomas Carlyle. The clearest contemporary ideological in-
centives to over-work actually come from humanistic psychologists such as
Abraham Maslow. A supposedly natural drive towards 'self-development' is
very easily co-opted into realizing one's potential through constant effort in
the busy workplace.

Volf's own proposal is to replace the idea of vocation with the notion of charism.
A portfolio of gifts (or charisms) is to be employed and discovered in our work.
Now the work of a doctor requires a long training period, which may be at odds
with the idea of discovering a 'gift' of healing. Charism seems to neglect the need
to work at, and grow into, one's profession. By contrast, vocation captures well
the sense that I have been summoned to some activity which stands over and
against me, an activity that will shape me as I give myself to it. Vocation explains
the sense that 'I am a doctor,' not merely that 'I have gifts in the medical field.'

Renewing the Idea of Vocation
One of the major problems with the idea of vocation, as described thus far, is
that it is a flat, dehumanized concept. Talk of vocation seems to conjure up an
image of the individual pitted against the potentially limitless task of serving
humanity. Vocation, in this sense, is experienced as a heavy load. Vocation needs,
rather, to be conceived as a three-dimensional relationship between persons.

The idea of a calling typically seems to presume three parties: someone who
calls, someone who is called and those to whom the called is sent.[30] The relationship
between the three parties is established, not through the bureaucratic and
impersonal terms of a contract, but through the more personal and supple terms
of what we may term a covenant.[31] On hearing the summons, the individual
responds with a promise to obey. The terms of this promise literally constitute the
individual as a 'professional,' one who professes. The subsequent work of the
professional is then authorized and governed by the terms of the covenant, the
terms of his or her profession.

Something approximating to this threefold structure is assumed in the form of
the ancient Hippocratic Oath. The doctor says, 'I swear by [the gods and god-
desses], making them my witnesses, that I will fulfil according to my ability and

---

2 9 See further Goldingay and Innes, *op cit*, p 17 and *Unemployment and the Future of Work*, (cited
above) which paints a picture of a society divided between those who overwork and those who
have no work.

3 0 The vocation to be a hermit seems an obvious exception. Here the relationship between caller
and called is strongly in the foreground. The individual is called away from fellow human
beings rather than to them.

3 1 The importance of 'covenant' for understanding the identity of the doctor has been impres-
sively set out by William May, *op cit*, and more recently by Neil Messer in *The Therapeutic
Covenant* (Grove Ethical Series No 103, Cambridge: Grove Books, 1996).

judgment this oath and this covenant.'[32] There then follow a series of clauses relating to the doctor's commitments to third parties—in this case not limited to patients but including also some quite specific commitments to his children, his teachers and his teachers' children.

A typical contemporary medical oath loses the divine referent, has general rather than specific responsibilities to teachers and includes a general clause about the duty to serve humanity.[33] The impression is given of a one-dimensional and unlimited obligation on behalf of the doctor to a boundless need. The idea of a calling without a caller actually becomes a heavy burden to bear. For what happens without a real caller is that the doctor tends to hear the summons as issued by those whom he or she serves, or by society at large. The calling then becomes an unequal agreement between an ocean of need and one individual. It is not surprising that, in these circumstances, doctors look for contracts which will limit their responsibility. It may well be that a calling without a caller is too dangerous for the one who is called. Vocation in this truncated sense might be a concept we are better off without.

A truer notion of vocation can only be established with the recovery of a more three-dimensional understanding of the calling. For the Christian, the one who calls is God. The primary calling (the spiritual calling) is into covenant relationship with God. Thereby, the Christian is set in an ordered and humane way of life orientated to the person's good. This way of life includes important principles concerning our work, most notably the principle of sabbath rest. Work is kept within ordered bounds.

The two fundamental commands which structure this covenant relationship with God are, firstly, the command to love God, and, secondly, the command to love our neighbour as ourselves. One of the most important effects of Luther's doctrine of vocation is to insist that earthly work is a means of fulfilling the *second* commandment, not the *first*. It would never, on Luther's understanding, be possible to love God adequately solely by working. Work in the service of others is important, but not of *first* importance. Luther's doctrine excludes a religion of total work. It insists that there is something more to life than work which ultimately gives work its meaning and purpose. Working in the service of others is placed within the wider context of our love and worship of God.

Worship of God sets bounds to work. The duty to worship God is a prior requirement which gives moral strength to resist tendencies to deify work—either through oppressive ideological use of 'vocation' by superiors or through our own upwardly spiralling self-development and self-immersion in work. Our identity is defined by our relationship with God, not primarily by our work. Self-realization comes as a by-product from enjoyable and valuable work done for our fellows which does not violate this primary relationship.

Our vocation then works itself out in covenant commitments not only to 'our

32 Cited in Phillips and Dawson, *Doctors' Dilemmas*, p 192.
33 For example the Declaration of Geneva cited above.

teachers' but also to 'our patients.' Within the former category, doctors owe loyalty both to colleagues and also to those who have paid for their training, namely society at large. This involves a commitment to careful stewardship of the finite resources with which society endows the doctor, most notably the use of his or her own time. Against this are commitments to the health and welfare of individual patients who come under the doctor's care.

The doctor's relationship with his or her patients is best understood as a *professional* one, not as a contractual one.[34] In a business contract, two parties freely enter into an agreement for their own interest. By contrast, a professional man or woman ought to be guided by the interests of the one whom he or she serves. The doctor puts herself in my position, considers my interests, does the best she can for me and advises me what would be best from my point of view. (What seems like an increasing tendency amongst doctors to give patients a series of options from which they can choose is, on this understanding, an unwillingness fully to shoulder professional responsibility.) The doctor defends her decisions by reference to the ideals and standards of her profession, not instructions from a superior or the pressures of the market. It is, in large part, the sense of *vocation* to the profession which gives one the moral authority and strength to do this.

The professional, of course, has a responsibility to avail herself of the best possible technical knowledge. She has a duty to keep her skills and knowledge up to date. But she is more than a *technician*, providing such skills, expertise and technique as someone demands and is willing to pay for. A professional is one capable of mature judgment.

This renewed account of vocation is an explicitly Christian one. Medicine grew up in a Christian culture, and this culture provided the ethos within which a commitment to medicine made sense. Those with other faiths or none will need to find alternative ways forward in considering the problem of sustaining commitment to medicine. However, *it seems to us doubtful whether the medical profession can be sustained for an indefinite period without an adequate meta-ethical background of some kind*. If we are right, then the task of recovering a meta-ethic is a crucial one. All contributions to debate at this level, from whatever perspective they come, are to be welcomed.

---

3 4 See J R Lucas, *Responsibility* (Oxford: OUP, 1993) p 193ff.

6
A New Vocation

The heart of medicine must remain the covenantal relationship between the doctor and patient. In this encounter the doctor seeks to understand the patient's symptoms and concerns in the light of his or her professional knowledge and experience. The patient offers information and allows a physical examination and any further procedures as the doctor advises. An agreed course of action is identified and the consequences of that plan are shared with all interested parties. When curative treatment is no longer possible, palliation and support are offered until the patient ceases to require it or until another, more appropriate, practitioner takes over the care.

When doctors work in teams with other health care professionals, this individualized doctor-patient relationship is no longer so clear cut. Arrangements for demarcating responsibilities need to be made, particularly when team members go off-duty or on holiday. The era of the 24-hour-a-day, 365-days-per-year doctor has gone. The loss of this approach to individual care has caused angst for many who see their work as more than a 'job.' For them the calling to be a doctor means giving everything. The word 'vocation' helps them to describe their feelings—no mere occupation or job governed by contract, but something much nobler and finer.

Yet the consequences of over-commitment to medicine cannot be too strongly emphasized. The high rate of suicide, alcohol and drug addiction and family breakdown within the medical profession is well documented.[35] Over-stretched individuals are hardly the best carriers of the message of health to the wider community! Inevitably the work of a doctor will be stressful, but this, surely, is even more reason for a balance to be established between working, relaxing and sharing in family life. Doctors have responsibilities not just to their patients, but also to those around them, to themselves, and to God.

Within the profession there is a tendency to criticize some newer practitioners as lazy or uncommitted. Maybe this new generation, Generation 'Why?,' is the sensible one, which seeks a proper balance between home and hospital, personal health and the health centre. Each generation must listen to the stories of the other. The challenge to government and profession alike is to manage the gap between the expectations of old and new and to provide adequately for patient health in a climate of falling doctor hours.

Ultimately, how the doctor responds to pain and suffering in his or her relationships with patients remains the true, caring benchmark. Technology and management have their place. But by themselves they speak of tightly-defined

---

3 5 G Bennet, *The Wound and the Doctor: Healing, Technology and Power in Modern Medicine* (London: Secker and Warburg, 1987).

relationships based upon control and dependency. This fails to honour the gifts patients bring to the relationship—the vast amount of goodwill, trust and confidence they invest in their doctors. A much better model of the doctor-patient relationship involves open-endedness, trust and generosity.[36] This kind of relationship is more fittingly conceived as a covenant than a contract. The work which takes place within it is rightly and properly understood as a vocation—a vocation given its shape by the goodness and generosity of the One who calls.

3 6 So comments Hélène Cixous in Nicholas Fox, *Postmodernism, Sociology and Health* (Buckingham: Open University Press, 1993) p 68.